J. R. Carpenter

The Gathering Cloud

Uniformbooks 2017

for Jerome and Aphra,
my silver linings

First published 2017
Copyright © J. R. Carpenter
ISBN 978–1–910010–15–0

Uniformbooks
7 Hillhead Terrace, Axminster, Devon EX13 5JL
www.uniformbooks.co.uk

Trade distribution in the UK by Central Books
www.centralbooks.com

Printed and bound by T J International, Padstow, Cornwall

"The machine sighed, and a cloud-like shape began to appear above the rows of tubes. At first it was thin and wispy. Then it thickened and became opaque."

—Jerome Fletcher, *Escape from the Temple of Laughter.*

CONTENTS

On Media Meteorology

Every time it rains, media history soaks into our skin. Clouds and their seemingly light ephemeral nature are full of the chemical remnants of the ongoing industrial age, which some call the Anthropocene. Human science and technology have penetrated the hard geological substrates of our culture and made the air part of our chemical cultural history. Many prefer to think of the current information age as one of light, marked by the weightlessness of fibre optics and the speed of digital transactions, and yet it is also one of weight—of minerals, metals, energy consumption, and entropy.

The weather comes and goes but our enthusiasm for it persists. To speak of weather is to articulate a continuum between humans and their environment. It is what's high above our heads and what sustains life beneath our feet that should concern us most. A breath of air. We inhale the weather. We exhale it. We measure it, we paint it, we verbalise it, we speak and write poetry about it.

J. R. Carpenter's *The Gathering Cloud* is both a condensation of media history and a comment on the current environmental weight of clouds. This book reminds us that cloud computing is one of the backbones of contemporary culture. The particularly interesting thing about cloud computing is that it is so heavily about climate control: server farms are carefully managed environments that cater to the well-being of the machines that ignorantly and yet with high-speed accuracy convey the things we talk about online, from #lolcats to emails, from memes to alternative facts. Of course, clouds were technological long before cloud computing. As Carpenter writes, J. M. W. Turner's painting 'Rain, Steam and Speed' (1844) is about the meeting of a new technological world with the air of the planet: the exhaust of the steam trains and the massive factories that define the particular clouds of our era of climate change mix with air to create vast fields of waste, both visible and invisible.

Clouds are painted, engraved, and increasingly now also computed in weather simulations and forecast models that both holiday goers and the military follow keenly. Clouds and the weather have been continuously remediated through a history of visual technologies and strategies of representation, and still, as Carpenter points out, they resist a stable ontology. They resist a lot of things: they are made of constant perturbations, micro-movements, dynamic turbulence. This struggle with representation is not just about showing what's up there, but also bringing it back down here as material for analysis: nowadays, clouds are simulated again and again, and so return to digital cloud (computing) platforms.

Carpenter evokes the Greek philosophy of the four elements (earth, air, fire and water) as part of a media and visual history. As such, her project relates to recent work in both contemporary technological art and cultural theory interested in the environment. She draws upon John Durham Peters' *The Marvellous Clouds*, which starts investigations of media from their elemental existence as nature. As Peters argues, the sky has been for a long period considered as a place of media. Read as signs by ancient Babylonians, as exhalations by ancient Greek philosophers, only in our age of technical media has the sky become the object of another sort of analysis. The sky is where visual media starts, as light filtered through the atmospheric levels. But light is not the only element of interest. The other chemical realities of clouds must also be included in this story.

The Gathering Cloud presents a series of material transformations made visible through a media history executed as digital collage and print publication, hendecasyllabic verse, and critical essay. Carpenter's methodology as a writer is closely linked to the field of media archaeology (a field interested in artistic, surprising, experimental, and sometimes imaginary ways of understanding contemporary media culture though the past). But it would be as fair to call her work a poetic media meteorology: it shows the multiplicity of ways of writing about the sky, the digital cloud, and the climate changes that we are living through, revealing gaps between our concepts of and the realities of the environment. And don't be mistaken by the airy connotations of the word—the cloud is already well deep in our lungs as well as our minds.

An Index of Objects

aerosol
air
bird
body
bomb
breaker
carbon
cat
catastrophe
cloud
coal
computer
country
creature
dark
data
earth
electricity
elephant
eruption
eucalyptus
evening
exhalation
fir
fish
flood
fog
fur

gas
heaven
honey
journal
language
lightning
mist
mountain
painting
photograph
rain
river
sea
seawall
sky
smoke
specimen
storm
sun
sunset
thunder
vapour
war
waste
water
wave
weather
wind

February 2014

It's raining. It has always rained. We are silt
dwellers, tide chasers, puddles, floods, mud, streams.
The river runs brown topsoil down and out
to the sea. From a fir erupts a murmur
of starlings. By fir I also mean fur.
A pelt of needles, hackles raised. Storm force ten
at the river mouth. The scale only goes up
to twelve. After that the sky breaks. The fir comes
down and takes two youthful eucalyptus with it.

In response to the conveyor belt of storms
that battered south-western England early
in 2014, resulting in
catastrophic flooding in Somerset and
the destruction of the seawall and rail line
at Dawlish, in Devon, the Met Office's
chief scientist, Dame Julia Slingo,
publically stated that the prolonged spell
of rain, and the intensity and height of
the coastal waves was "very unusual".

She said: "We have records going back to
1766. We have seen some
exceptional weather, but nothing like this.
All evidence suggests a link to climate change."

20 THE GATHERING CLOUD

Following the news in the months after these storms
I was struck by the paradox presented
by attempts to evoke through the material
of language invisible forces such as
wind and rising temperatures which we can
only see indirectly through their affects.

I began collecting language pertaining
to weather from current news items and from
older sources including classical texts
and almanacs, private weather journals,
and past forecasts held at the National
Meteorological Library and
Archive at the Met Office in Exeter.

One thing I figured out pretty early on
in the course of this research is that it's hard
to study only one kind of weather.

On one page of one nineteenth-century
private weather journals held at the
Met Office Archive we may see thunder and
lightning, a meteor, lilacs, lily
of valley, and hyacinths in full blossom.

Hardly surprising then that classical ideas
about the weather now seem somewhat confused.

423 BCE

For most of human history the heavens
have served as a source of legitimacy,
providing meaning and orientation.
The sky is compass, calendar, map, and clock.

In *The Clouds*, a Greek comedy of ideas,
Aristophanes mocks the ancient notion
of the sky as a theatre of the gods.

The machine swings in SOCRATES in a basket.

Socrates descends *deus ex machina* from
his studies of the sky to the hard stage floor
where he is joined by a chorus of clouds,
patron goddesses of thinkers and layabouts.

I have to suspend my brain and mingle the
subtle essence of my mind with this air, which
is of the like nature, in order clearly
to penetrate the things of heaven. I should
have discovered nothing, had I remained on
the ground to consider from below the things
that are above; for the earth by its force
attracts the sap of the mind to itself.

350 BCE

Of the fashion and form of heaven, and of
the air, and the winds, Aristotle observes:

From the clouds there fall three types of bodies
formed by refrigeration—water, snow, and hail.

The exhalation from water into
air is vapour. Water falling in small drops
is drizzle; in larger drops, rain.
Mist is the residue of the condensation
of air into water, a sign of fine weather.

Moisture rises and falls as the sun moves.
As a river with a circular course rises
and falls, a mixture of water and air.
Thus the river Ocean flows round the earth.

The winds are the cause of the waves and not the
waves of winds. The winds produce the same effects
upon clouds in sky as sea upon shore.

When calm,
clouds are straight and fine like lines of breakers.

Clouds sweeping along with great noise close to the
earth strike fear into those that see them as
portents of some greater catastrophe.

The editor of the Loeb edition of
Aristotle's *Meteorologica*
observes that Aristotle is so far wrong
in nearly all his conclusions that they can,
it may with justice be said, have little more
than a passing antiquarian interest.

50 BCE

The Epicurean materialist
Lucretius attempted to improve upon
Aristotle's theory of atmospheric
exhalations based on the four elements
of earth, air, fire, and water, and their
associated interactive properties
of heat and coldness, of dryness and moisture.

Clouds cannot be composed of such dense bodies
as make up stones or logs, nor of such flimsy
ones as mist and drifting smoke, Lucretius reasoned.

The formation of clouds is due to sudden
coalescence of many flying atoms
of relatively rough material.

Clouds mimic mountains wafted through air by wind.
Clouds, like dangling fleeces, absorb water
when they are swept by the winds over the sea.

There are waves in the clouds that make a booming
sound when they break heavily, just as happens
in the wide sea when the surf is breaking.

Nothing can be created out of nothing.

The whole earth exhales a vaporous steam.

late 1300s

As Christianity spread throughout Europe
the scientific influence of ancient
authorities gave way to a conception
of all atmospheric activities as
signs of divine and moral intervention.

In the second half of the 14th century
an anonymously authored Christian text
called *The Cloude of Unknowyng* proposed that
God is a pure entity, beyond any
capacity of mental conception and
so without any definitive form.

If you want to gather all your desire
into one word that the mind can easily
retain, choose a short word rather than a long one.
Then fix it in your mind so it will remain.
Use it to beat upon the cloud of darkness
above you and to subdue all distractions,
consigning them to the cloud of forgetting.

God's cloud of unknowing can only be pierced
with a dart of longing love from the heart.

1475

In the long interval between Aristotle,
Lucretius, and the Enlightenment, clouds were
generally thought too changeable to be
scientifically quantifiable.

Even as classifying tendencies took hold
in the late Middle Ages, insects, worms, snails,
and other creatures that were not clearly birds, beasts
or fish presented peculiar problems
in classification. So did their products.
Honey, for instance, comes under the weather
phenomena in Book II of Megenberg's
Buch der Natur, 1475,
right after the cause of mildew.

1665

Robert Hooke, first Curator of Experiments
at the Royal Society of London,
attempted to develop a language of
observation, proposing an entire
vocabulary of recommended terms
for the sky's variety of vaporous states:

clear
a clear sky without clouds or exhalations

checkered
a sky with many great white round clouds
as are very usual in the summer months

hazy
a sky that looks whitish by reason
of the thickness of the higher parts of the air

thick
a sky whitened by company of vapours

hairy
a sky that has many, small, thin, and
high exhalations resembling locks of hair

watered
a sky with many high thin and small
clouds, called in some places a mackerel sky

waved
a sky where those clouds appear much bigger
and lower, but much after the same manner.

cloudy
when the sky has many thick dark clouds

lowering
when the sky has also underneath
many thick dark clouds which look to threaten rain

Hooke abandoned his meteorological journal after a few months at the chore.

1667

Margaret Cavendish, Duchess of Newcastle,
was the first woman to attend a meeting
of the Royal Society of London.
This dangerous experiment was met with
such protest from the male fellows it was not
repeated again for a few hundred years.

In her polemical *Observations on
Experimental Philosophy* published
the next year, she questioned the Baconian
notion of relentless mechanical progress.

Her science-fiction story, *The Blazing World*,
considered alternative futures of science.

1783

The spring days started out fair and temperate.
As the months wore on an unfamiliar
pattern was widely noticed, of increasingly
hot days followed by cold nights shrouded in
a strange sort of hovering opalescent fog
which grew steadily and progressively worse.
An accompanying sulphurous smell soon
settled everywhere, fouling the dry summer air.
As the haze spread, people sickened and violent
thunderstorms stirred in the thickening skies.
The news spread, through bulletins and letters.
All of Europe and half of Asia were
experiencing the same dispiriting
weather conditions, an unwholesomeness of air.

It was Benjamin Franklin who first made the
geological connection: four of the
world's most active volcanoes had recently
erupted, spewing clouds of ash and toxic gas.

Volcanic clouds suggest the solidity
of thousands of tons of incinerated
stone suspended impossibly in the air.

The largest eruptions can send millions of
tons of dust, ash, and sulphur compounds straight through
the troposphere, deep into the stratosphere
where they form suspended clouds of aerosols.

The first balloon ascents were staged in Paris
that same strange meteorological year.
Human flight would finally be achieved by
imitating not a bird but a cloud.

The balloon allowed the study of clouds
to enter an new phase of intimacy.

1786

In August of 1786,
the Royal Society published an
Account of a New Comet, by Caroline
Herschel, discoverer of eight comets in all.

The observational journal Herschel kept
for thirty years is one of the earliest
records of how science actually gets done.

1802

One December evening in 1802
the young and as yet unpublished Quaker,
chemist, and amateur meteorologist
Luke Howard presented a public lecture
On the Modifications of Clouds to the
Askesian Society in London—
a practically oriented and largely
non-conformist group dedicated to the
study and discussion of the burgeoning
field of experimental philosophy.

Over the course of an hour Howard put
forward both a new explanation of the
formation and lifespan of clouds and a
new methodological nomenclature.
In contrast to fixed Linnaean taxonomies—
all the rage in London at that moment—Howard's
deceptively simple classificatory
system allowed for continual movement.

The Latin names outlined in Howard's lecture
remain the definitive terms used today.

A Methodological Nomenclature

cirrus
a few threads pencilled, as it were, on the sky
increase in length as new threads are added
serving as stems to support numerous branches.
the increase is sometimes indeterminate

cumulus
at first, a small irregular spot appears
and moves along with the current next the earth
and rapidly grows to the size of mountains
then diminishes and totally disperses

stratus
a mean degree of density commonly
rests its inferior surface on water
this is properly a cloud of the night time
an inundation to cover dark country

cirrocumulous
fibres collapse and pass into round masses
their texture now no longer discernible
this change takes place throughout the whole cloud at once
accelerated by others approaching

cirrostratus
the fibres subside to a horizontal
presenting the appearance of shoals of fish
distinctly extenuated towards the edge.
on this account, worthy of investigation

cumulostratus
showing dark against the lighter cloud above
the former cloud continues discernible
this state of things continues but a short time
the cloud speedily becomes denser and spreads

nimbus, or *cumulonimbus*
appearances are but imperfectly seen
at a greater altitude a thin light veil
lower clouds unite in a uniform sheet
the rain then commences, arriving from windward

1802

Meanwhile, in France, an employee of the
Muséum national d'histoire naturelle
Jean-Baptiste Lamarck had spent the early months
of 1802 devising a system
remarkably similar to Luke Howard's.
He observed that clouds have certain general
forms which are not at all dependant upon
chance but rather a state of affairs which it
would be useful to recognise and determine.

He proposed the following five cloud families:

en forme de voile (hazy clouds)
attroupés (massed clouds)
pommels (dappled clouds)
en balayeurs (broom-like clouds)
groupés (grouped clouds)

He later added the additional terms:

nuages moutonnées (flocked clouds)
nuages en lambeaux (torn clouds)
nuages en barres (banded clouds)
nuages en coureurs (running clouds)

Couched in a pastoral vernacular and
lacking in the precision necessary
for the foundation of a scientific language
Lamarck's parochial terms never caught on.

Furthermore, unfortunately for Lamarck
Napoléon disliked him intensely.

1803

An expanded version of Howard's lecture
on clouds was published almost immediately
in Alexander Tilloch's massively
influential *Philosophical Magazine*,
appearing in three parts in 1803.

This essay was illustrated with engraved
plates based upon Howard's watercolour sketches.
Translated into crosshatching, Howard's studies
lost subtlety, but gained fixity, moving
them toward the diagrammatic scientific.

1865

From the time of its first presentation as
an oral lecture to the definitive
print publication of Howard's essay,
prepared by his sons in 1865,
the year after his death, the technology
of image-making underwent great change.
19th-century innovations in book
making saw both the introduction of steel
plate engraving and photo-mechanical
illustration. At the same time, scientists
turned toward self-registering techniques such as
making plaster casts and taking photographs,
toward a new standard of documentation
supposed to be free from human interference.

The engraved images which illustrated
Howard's essay were manufactured rather
than mechanically reproduced. In them we
see a tussle between artistic, linguistic,
and scientific sensibilities—a
tension between accuracy and atmosphere.

In the body of the text of his essay,
Howard used painterly terms of reference
such as 'in the foreground,' 'in the distance,'
and 'at picture top' to engage readers in
his new scientific terminology.

Even as Howard's coolly scientific
classification of untamed nature
took hold, the imagery with which it was
associated was increasingly bound
by the conventions of Romanticism,
the rugged ruralism of the picturesque.

Howard's studied naturalism, based on
close observation, intruded into the
traditional domain of landscape painting
as a standard of observation, marking
a movement away from the idealized
toward the mathematically quantified.

1821–1822

Clouds pose peculiar problems for painting.
Their voluminous shapes defy perspective
illustrating the maxim that there is
nothing so productive as a law to transgress.

In a series of cloud studies undertaken
by John Constable on Hampstead Heath over
the course of two summers the methods of an
old art, landscape painting, and a new science,
meteorology, were combined in one outlook.

Constable applied minerals of the earth—
manganese, mercury, chromium, oxide—
to modifications of clouds in the sky.
He wrote notes on weather conditions on the
back of his sketches whilst waiting for them to dry.

1844

J. M. W. Turner's oil painting 'Rain, Steam
and Speed—The Great Western Railway', shows a steam
train engulfed in a cloud of its own making,
mixing natural and scientific,
coal-fired steam and air-borne particulate.

The train steams over a rail bridge designed by
the great Victorian civil engineer
Isambard Kingdom Brunel, who also built
the rail line and seawall at Dawlish, Devon.

1859

Running parallel to the open sea at
the base of red sandstone cliffs for four miles,
the seawall at Dawlish has always been prone
to damage during high tides and rough weather.

In 1859 the sea broke through the line.
The Illustrated London News reported:
"Such was the terrific force of the impelled
water that along the seawall and railway
huge coping-stones, probably averaging
one ton each, were tossed about like corks…"

1896

Clouds resist ontology. As a result
of the long exposure times required by
early cameras, early photographs show
skies wiped white by clouds moving at speed overhead.

By the time of the publication of the
first *International Cloud Atlas* in
1896, photography was a
viable alternative to engraving.

In the first edition, the towering
cumulonimbus was cloud number nine.
The addition of new sub-categories
has since altered this sequence but the ecstatic
expression of being on cloud nine persists.

1856

The scientist, inventor, and equal rights
campaigner Eunice Foote conducted a
simple experiment: she filled glass jars with
different gases, and put them out in the sun.
She found that the jar containing water
vapour and carbon dioxide heated the most.

When presenting the results of this research
on what we now call greenhouse gases
to The American Association
for the Advancement of Science, she observed:
"more carbon dioxide in the atmosphere
would trap more heat, thus making the earth warmer".

Average carbon dioxide levels in the
atmosphere have since increased by over
110 parts per million.

1832

The term 'fog' was first used in reference to
uncertainty experienced in war by
the Prussian military analyst
Carl von Clausewitz in 1832:
Three quarters of the factors upon which all
action in military operations
are based are wrapped in a fog of uncertainty.
He also used the words 'twilight' and 'moonlight'
to describe the state of ignorance in which
commanders and combatants find themselves.

Military forces try to reduce the
fog of war through gathering intelligence.

1918

During World War I, Heidegger served as a
weatherman on the western front, near Verdun.
From a wooden tower he observed daily
wind directions and speeds, collecting all the
data necessary for the deployment
of artillery, aircraft, and poison gas.
Heidegger's rank was Luftschiffer—
he was literally a captain of the air.
The Heideggerian trope of vigilance
as a paramount ethical duty was
born during these months of scanning the sky for signs.

Heidegger argues that the distinguishing
characteristic of modern science is
mathematics—that which can be learnt by taking.
We take what we ourselves somehow already have:

a vapour trail, a radio wave, a bomb
blast, a cloud of smoke, of deadly poison gas.

Modern warfare is waged in a theatre of air.

1933–1948

Throughout World War II, Heidegger was involved
with the Nazi Party. For seventy years
his many apologists and acolytes
have insisted this weakness in character
has no bearing upon his philosophical oeuvre.
The recent publication of Heidegger's
black notebooks confirmed anti-Semitism
lies at the core of his philosophy.

In perhaps his best-known poem, 'Todesfug', or
'Death Fugue', written in 1948, the
Romanian-born German-language poet
Paul Celan bewailed victims of holocaust
ovens whose only graves were in the clouds:

This Death is a master from Germany
He calls out more darkly now scrape your strings.
You'll rise then as smoke to the sky. You'll have
a grave then in the clouds. There you won't lie too cramped.

In 2001 Rüdiger Safranski
published a biography of Heidegger
called *Ein Meister aus Deutschland*
a line borrowed from Celan's cloud grave poem.

1945

For decades a famous photo circulated
of the most iconic cloud in history,
the mushroom cloud over Hiroshima.
Watermarked 'Hiroshima (atomic) strike',
nuclear experts now say the towering plume
is not a mushroom cloud at all, but rather,
a cloud of billowing smoke rising from the
raging firestorms that followed the explosion.

1922–1996

The digital cloud is older than we think.

In 1922 Lewis Fry Richardson
proposed a telegraphic network linking
human computers, or mathematicians,
designed to aid in the prediction of weather.

The first digital computers were built to
decode air-borne encrypted messages
intercepted from wireless transmissions
and to calculate ballistic trajectories.

Engineers have used the symbol of a cloud
to represent any unspecifiable
network since as early as 1970.

The term 'cloud computing' first appears in print
in the *MIT Technology Review*
in 1996.

The digital cloud is formed of fine droplets
of data gathering information from air.

The Gathering Cloud

luckysoap.com/thegatheringcloud

Mohoua ochrocephala
USNM 109195

Notiomystis cincta
USNM 172402

Petroica macrocephala
USNM 109208

Acanthisitta chloris

Petroica phoenicea
USNM 425214

Petroica multicolor

Petroica boodang

Petroica rosea
USNM 121274

goodenovii
121275

2 cm

67

Frontispiece

A sky full of peculiar specimens
of dense clouds shrouded in a gloomy distance.

Forms assumed by clouds gathering for thunder
storms are highly characteristic in structure.

The Cloud is an airily deceptive name
connoting a floating world far removed from
the physical realities of data.

The avian skin collection held at the
Natural History Museum in London
contains almost seven-hundred and fifty
thousand specimens of birds, representing
ninety-five per cent of the world's nine-thousand-
and six-hundred known species. The Division
of Birds at the Smithsonian in Washington
contains a further six-hundred and forty
thousand specimens. How many more birds have
been captured and tagged and stored in The Cloud?

The extreme heat of the lightning bolt is what
produces the crashing rumble of thunder.

Lightning is electricity passing through
air due to a cloud developing regions
of differing electrical charge within.

Data centres worldwide use thirty billion
watts of electricity annually.
Most of that is spent on avoiding downtime.
Guarding against the event of grid failure
banks of generators emit diesel exhaust.

If all the data centres constituted
a country of their own it would be the fifth
most power-hungry country in the world.

x 10

Plate No.1

Above the horizon, some large cumulus
receiving on their tops a cirrostratus.

In the blue sky, the cirrus fair-weather shapes.
At left, the feather is rare but genuine.

The Cloud is just someone else's computer,
that's what the coffee mugs and fridge magnets say.
But what does that mean?
How much does The Cloud weigh?

The cloud formed when we exhale on a cold day
contains at least four per cent water molecules.

A typical white fluffy cumulus cloud
stores a half gram of water per square metre.
That works out to about half a million kilos.
A cloud the weight of one hundred elephants.

To minuscule cumulus water droplets
air in an upwelling thermal below them
is as dense as honey is to a pebble
five thousandths of a millimetre across.

The better the infrastructure works, the more
likely it is to be taken for granted.

The New York Stock Exchange, produces up to
two-thousand gigabytes of data per day.

One hundred hours of video are
uploaded to YouTube every minute.
A billion hours are watched every day.

An estimated 1.8 trillion
gigabytes of digital information
are created and stored globally each year
by ordinary consumers with no sense
that data is physical and storing it
has a direct impact on the environment.

If the internet weren't so important
we could scale back our use of it, like we've done
with Styrofoam containers and aerosol cans.

The Cloud is an increasingly essential
element of infrastructure powering
industry, government, finance and commerce,
as fundamental to us as plumbing and roads.

The scale of the cloud should fill us with urgency.

Plate No.2

This picture presents the commencement of cloud
mixed with objects common to a landscape.

Stratus evening mist creeping through the valley
rising to become shortly a dense body
resting with a level surface on the ground
possibly covering the country with fog.

Above, in the blue sky, features of cirrus.

Terrestrial stratus is linked to absence.
This is properly a cloud of the night-time
an inundation to cover dark country.

The sun obscures the stars. The night reveals truth.

The fog comes on cute pics of little cat feet.
Four million feline photos are shared each day.
#lolcats track carbon footprints across The Cloud.

Tech giants Apple, Amazon, and Microsoft
power their twenty-first century clouds with
dirty nineteenth-century coal energy.
Assessing the field is complicated by
the secretive nature of the industry.

The term The Cloud refers to a cultural fantasy.

We walk on the bed of the sea of the air.

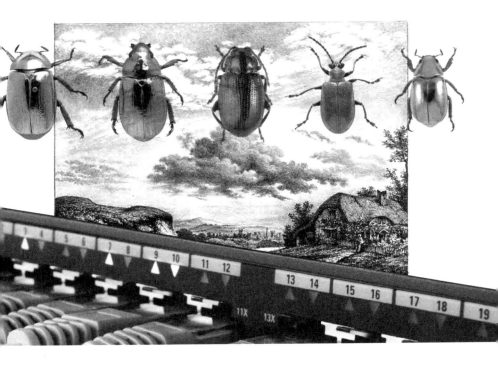

Plate No.3

In the foreground, a cumulus is breaking
in the sky part of a fine summer's evening.

More distant, to the left, shows cloud that remained.

Next, above, at the greatest elevation,
at picture top, a fine cirrocumulus.

Aisles of servers with amber, blue, and green
lights flashing hold our old email attachments.

We have saved too many memories to lose.
Snapshots from nearly forgotten vacations,
five-thousand four-hundred and seventy-five
sunsets stored forever in Cloud formations.

Data centres constitute a pivotal
piece of post-photographic equipment.
Image-driven digital socializing
is enabled by stationary servers.

An email may travel thousands of miles
and pass through multiple data centres
to send a photograph across the street.

Plate No.4

A fine specimen of cumulostratus
illustrating the mutual attraction
of a cumulus and a cirrostratus.

In the blue sky, above, are cirri tending
to the change which makes them cirrocumulus.

The picture a fine evening after showers.

The fibres subside to a horizontal
presenting the appearance of shoals of fish
distinctly extenuated towards the edge.
On this account, worthy of investigation.

Digital media infrastructures
are successfully hiding in plain sight.

Microsoft is forging ahead with a plan
to create underwater data centres
that would reduce the cost of cooling servers
and provide shelter and warmth for sea creatures,
and possibly going so far as to
disperse nutrients for sea life to feed on.

We treat the air as an abode of the endless
an infinite receptacle for pollution.

The Cloud is the premier receptacle
for backup dumps, archaic, obsolete data.

The language of The Cloud is a barrier.

Both waste and vastness derive from the Latin
vastus—desolate, but also expansive.

Plate No.5

A nimbus or rain-cloud on the horizon
letting fall showers at moderate distance.

Two clouds, as yet in sunshine, show forwardness
by their expansion, progress toward the same state.

Nimbostratus revels in incessant rain.
Clouds and rain clean the air of pollutants.

The cumulonimbus contains energy
equivalent to ten Hiroshima-sized bombs.

The cloud's complex evolving structure makes it
feel almost like a living organism.

The digital cloud actively erases
its own historicity; like its namesake
it constructs itself through pure fluctuation.

The Cloud spreads beyond the edges of the page
a topography of our fears and desires.

Readily available recovery
makes disaster constantly imaginable.
Backups stored in The Cloud wait as if asleep
for a catastrophe that may never come.

When did computing come to feel personal?
When we stopped counting the cost of computation?
Like a muzzled creature, the cloud strains to be
more than it is, its sights on larger quarry.

This sky is one of a number of sketches
by the author of these modifications
illustrating a preponderance of white space.

Modifications on The Gathering Cloud

In 2015 I submitted a proposal based on my as yet amorphous research on the intertwined topics of language, weather, and climate change to the Dot Award— an annual prize sponsored by if:book and Bournemouth University that supports writing using the web in imaginative and collaborative ways.

I did not know then what form the final work would take, only that I wanted to attempt to address climate change by picturing through language something of the absences left by wind.

Winning the Dot Award enabled me to peruse this research in a freer way than I might otherwise have been able to.

The Gathering Cloud was commissioned by NEoN Digital Arts Festival, Dundee, UK, 9–13 November 2016.

The theme of NEoN 2016 was 'The Spaces We're In'. The co-curators Sarah Cook and Donna Holford-Lovell write: Physical urban space and virtual information space are inseparably intertwined. How does being digital change our sense of our spatial surroundings? Can we animate the hybrid spaces in-between? Is there negative space in cyberspace?

When the curators approached me with this theme I was in the midst of packing to move house. Surrounded by boxes of books and papers, old photographs, floppy disks, CDs, hard drives, and tangles of miscellaneous cables, I knew immediately that I wanted to call attention to the physicality of so-called 'cloud' storage.

I'd written on the materiality of the internet and the complex relations between biological and digital memory in previous work, but the scale of the digital cloud seemed too vast to think about in terms of the human body. I knew I had to think bigger. I turned to the clouds in the sky.

The Gathering Cloud aims to address the environmental impact of so-called 'cloud' computing and storage through the overtly oblique strategy of calling attention to the materiality of the clouds in the sky. Both kinds of clouds are commonly perceived to be infinite, at once vast and immaterial; both, decidedly, are not.

The Gathering Cloud gathers fragments of text from Howard's classic essay *On the Modifications of Clouds* as well as from more recent online articles and books on media theory and the environment. A bibliography of these textual sources is printed in the back of this book.

These found text fragments are pared down into hypertextual hendecasyllabic verses situated within six surreal animated gif collages composed of the illustrations from Howard's essay and images appropriated from publicly accessible cloud storage services including Flickr and Google Images.

The cognitive dissonance between the cultural fantasy of cloud storage and the hard facts of its environmental impact is bridged, in part, through the constant evocation of animals: four million cute cat pics, one hundred elephants, countless specimens of stuffed birds, one USB fish.

The portions of this text based on Luke Howard's descriptions of illustrations were first performed during the South West Poetry Tour, which took place 1–8 August 2016. My thanks and curses to Annabel Banks for suggesting the hendecasyllabic constraint which has shaped all subsequent web, print, and performance iterations of this work.

A zine iteration of *The Gathering Cloud* colour printed on A3–sized paper and shared through gift, trade, mail art, and small press economies further confuses the scant boundaries between animal and mineral, physical and digital, scarcity and waste.

The zine iteration of *The Gathering Cloud* was reproduced in *Hack Circus 12*, a journal based in Sheffield, UK.

The Gathering Cloud launched with a performance at a Pecha Kucha Night held in Dundee on the 8th of November, on the night of the US elections. I hadn't intended for the title to sound quite so ominous.

In light of recent political events, now more than ever we need to find ways to talk about the enormity of climate change in human terms we can understand and act upon.

The Gathering Cloud was awarded the New Media Writing Prize 2016, an annual award now in its seventh year founded by Jim Pope and supported by if:book and Bournemouth University, UK.

The Gathering Cloud was an Editor's Pick for the Saboteur Awards 2017, an annual award that celebrates indie literature in all its forms.

Bibliography

Data, dates, images, ideas, words, and whole hendecasyllabic phrases in this book have been found in, informed by, and borrowed from the following print and digital sources:

Anonymous, *The Cloud of Unknowing*. [late 1300s]

Aristophanes, *Clouds / Wasps / Peace*. Lobe Classical Library, Harvard University Press, 1998. [423 BCE]

Aristotle, *Meteorologica*. Lobe Classical Library, Harvard University Press, 1952. [350 BCE]

BBC News 'Met Office: Evidence "suggests climate change link to storms"' *BBC News* website. (9 February 2014) accessed 3 March 2017. www.bbc.co.uk/news/uk-politics-26084625

Margaret Cavendish, *The Blazing World and Other Writings*. London: Penguin Classics, 2004. [1666]

Paul Celan, *Selections*. ed. Pierre Joris. University of California Press, 2004.

Jerome Fletcher, *Escape from the Temple of Laughter*. London: Scholastic, 1994.

James Glanz, 'Power, Pollution, and the Internet', *The New York Times*, (22 September 2012) accessed 24 March 2017. www.nytimes.com/2012/09/23/technology/data-centers-waste-vast-amounts-of-energy-belying-industry-image.html

Richard Hamblyn, *The Invention of Clouds: How an Amateur Meteorologist Forged the Language of the Skies*. London: Picador, 2001.

Richard Holmes, 'The Royal Society's lost women scientists' *The Guardian*. (21 November 2010) Accessed 22 February 2017. www.theguardian.com/science/2010/nov/21/royal-society-lost-women-scientists

Luke Howard, *On the Modifications of Clouds*. London: John Churchill & Sons, 1865. [1803]

Tung-Hui Hu, *A Prehistory of the Cloud*, MIT Press, 2015.

Boris Jardine, 'Made real: artifice and accuracy in nineteenth-century scientific illustration' in *Science Museum Group Journal* Autumn 2014 issue 2. Accessed 26 January 2017. journal.sciencemuseum.ac.uk/browse/issue-02/made-real/

Friedrich Kittler, 'Towards an Ontology of Media', in *Theory, Culture & Society* March/May 2009 vol.26 no.2–3, SAGE, LA, London, New Delhi, & Singapore.

Lucretius, *The Nature of the Universe*. London: Penguin Classics, 1951. [55 BCE]

Konrad von Megenberg, *Das Buch der Natur*. Augsburg, 1475.

Peter Moore, *The Weather Experiment: The Pioneers who Sought to See the Future*. London: Vintage, 2015.

Philip Oltermann, 'Heidegger's "black notebooks" reveal antisemitism at core of his philosophy', *The Guardian*. (13 March 2014) accessed 16 February 2017. www.theguardian.com/books/2014/mar/13/martin-heidegger-black-notebooks-reveal-nazi-ideology-antisemitism

Jussi Parikka, *A Geology of Media*. Minnesota Press, 2015.

John Durham Peters, *The Marvelous Clouds: Toward a Philosophy of Elemental Media*. University of Chicago Press, 2015.

Gavin Pretor-Pinney, Gavin, *The Cloudspotter's Guide*, London: Sceptre, 2007.

Lewis Fry Richardson, *Weather prediction by numerical process*. Cambridge University Press, 1922.

Lisa Robertson, *The Weather*. Vancouver: New Star Books, 2011.

Rudiger Safanski, *Ein Meister aus Deutschland: Heidegger und seine Zeit*. Fischer Taschenbuch, 2001.

Further reading about The Gathering Cloud

NeoN Speaks with J. R. Carpenter (19 October 2016) www.northeastofnorth.com/neon-speaks-jr-carpenter/

Jussi Parikka (2016) 'J. R. Carpenter's The Gathering Cloud' in *Machinology*. (12 November 2016) accessed 16 February 2017. jussiparikka.net/2016/11/12/j-r-carpenters-the-gathering-cloud/

Prize winners announced for the New Media Writing Prize awards ceremony at Bournemouth University (19 January 2017). www1.bournemouth.ac.uk/news/2017-01-19/prize-winners-announced-new-media-writing-prize-awards-ceremony-bournemouth-university

NEoN commission wins New Media Writing Prize (27 January 2017). www.northeastofnorth.com/neon-digital-arts-festival-commission-wins-new-media-writing-prize/

Acknowledgements

Thanks to the curators, co-ordinators, editors, writers, artists, audiences, and volunteers at the following organisations: NEoN Digital Arts, Creative Dundee, Hospitalfield, if:book, the New Media Writing Prize, the Informatics Lab at the Met Office, the South West Poetry Tour, Hack Circus, Kaleider, Land / SCAPE, Future Imperfect, the Saboteur Awards, ELO Porto, and Uniformbooks.

Special thanks to Sarah Cook, Donna Holford-Lovell, Michael Saunby, Kay Lovelace, Jussi Parikka, Lisa Robertson, Chris Meade, Jim Pope, Claire Trévien, Colin Sackett, and Jerome Fletcher.

LISA ROBERTSON

after cloud

cloud

cloudberry cloud-burst cloud-capped clouded
cloudless cloud-rack clouds cloud-scape cloudy clout-nail cloven-footed cloven-
hooved clove-oil clover clover-field clove-tree clown clownery clownish
club clubbable club-building club-hammer clubhouse club-law club-length clubman
club-moss club-room club-root clubs club-shaped clubwoman clumpfoot cluster
cluster-bug clustered clutch-lever clutch-plate clutch-rod Cnaeus Cnidus coach-box
coach-horse coach-house coachman coachstand coachwork coagency coal
coal-black coal-consumption coal-dust coalesce
coalescence coalescent

coalfield

whatever

gathers things together whatever gathers people
together and thinking together given the great long whooshing passage of
time wind economies technologies beliefs and whatever gathers a sentence together
and whatever a poem is both physics and mysterious and so we wish to read which
is to say to interpret and to collect and to suppose and to wander and to rest a little
while in contemplation that glorious lost art because before the irruption there must
be contemplation even most fanciful but also at times angriest or with deepest
worry because we love these skies this clod on which we perch
this muscular desire which is

heart